M000110432

LANGUAGE ARTS 310

CONTENTS

Author:	**Patsy J. Ressler, M.A.Ed.**
Editor-in Chief:	Richard W. Wheeler, M.A.Ed.
Editor:	Joyce R. Davis
Consulting Editor:	Rudolph Moore, Ph.D.
Revision Editor:	Alan Christopherson, M.S.

Alpha Omega Publications®

804 N. 2nd Ave. E., Rock Rapids, IA 51246-1759

© MCMXCVI by Alpha Omega Publications, Inc. All rights reserved.
LIFEPAC is a registered trademark of Alpha Omega Publications, Inc.

All trademarks and/or service marks referenced in this material are the property of their respective owners. Alpha Omega Publications, Inc. makes no claim of ownership to any trademarks and/or service marks other than their own and their affiliates', and makes no claim of affiliation to any companies whose trademarks may be listed in this material, other than their own.

Learn with our friends:

When you see me, I will help your teacher explain the exciting things you are expected to do.

When you do actions with me, you will learn how to write, draw, match words, read, and much more.

You and I will learn about matching words, listening, drawing, and other fun things in your lessons.

LANGUAGE ARTS 310

You have learned a great deal this year in your Language Arts LIFEPACs. In Language Arts LIFEPAC® 310, you will review the skills that you have learned.

If you are able to do this LIFEPAC, you will know that you have learned the Language Arts skills well. You might be surprised and happy to find out just how much you have learned this year.

 **Objectives**

Read these objectives. They will tell you what you will be able to do when you have finished this LIFEPAC.

1. You will be able to write the events of a story in sequence.
2. You will be able to use context clues.
3. You will be able to mark the long and short vowels of words.
4. You will be able to recognize complete sentences.
5. You will be able to read a map.
6. You will be able to follow written directions.
7. You will be able to capitalize and punctuate sentences correctly.
8. You will be able to write a good paragraph and a letter.
9. You will be able to find four parts of speech in sentences.

10. You will be able to tell the main idea and the supporting details of a paragraph.

11. You will be able to tell the cause and effect in written work and predict the outcome.

12. You will be able to tell the difference between fiction and nonfiction.

13. You will be able to tell how to use a dictionary, atlas, and an encyclopedia.

14. You will be able to spell many words.

15. You will be able to write in cursive handwriting.

ability (u bil′ u tē). Power to do.

announce (u nouns′). Say.

cafetorium (kaf u tôr′ ē um). Room used for lunch and meetings.

chores (chôrz). Odd jobs.

clarinet (klar u net′). Musical instrument shaped like a tube, played by blowing on a mouthpiece and covering holes with fingers.

copied (kop′ ēd). One thing made just like another one.

eternity (i ter′ nu tē). Time without beginning or end.

general (jen′ ur ul). Officer of high rank.

member (mem′ bur). Person who belongs to a group.

nervous (ner′ vus). Tense or fearful.

organized (ôr' gun īzd). Put together in an orderly way.

popular (pop' yu lur). Pleasing to many people.

private (prī ' vit). Not shared with others.

program (prō' gram). A play or something given for a group of people.

requires (ri kwīrz'). Has need of.

scored (skôrd). Points made.

sports (spôrts). Games.

students (stü' dunts). People in school.

vacant (vā' kunt). Empty; not having anything in it.

yarn (yärn). Thread used in knitting or weaving.

These words will appear in **boldface** (darker print) the first time they are used.

Pronunciation Key: hat, āge, cãre, fär; let, ēqual, tėrm; it, ice; hot, ōpen, ôrder; oil; out; cup, půt, rūle; child; long; thin; /ŦH/ for then; /zh/ for measure; /u/ represents /a/ in about, /e/ in taken, /i/ in pencil, /o/ in lemon, and /u/ in circus.

I. SECTION ONE

In this section you will review sequencing and using context clues. Long and short vowel rules are reviewed to help you remember how vowels are pronounced. A short review on sentences is included. You will practice handwriting and review spelling words from three LIFEPACs.

yarn   (yärn)   Thread used in knitting or weaving.

Ask your teacher to say these words with you.
Teacher check _____

                                    Initial   Date

READING FOR COMPREHENSION

This story, "The Babysitter," will help you review some important comprehension skills—sequencing and using context clues. As you read, pay attention to the order in which things happen.

The Babysitter

Mary Jo was sitting with her two-year-old brother. Her mother had asked her to watch him while she planned the next meeting of the garden club.

Mary Jo had Jimmy on the rug in her room, reading <u>The Alphabet Book</u> to him. Jimmy didn't move. He loved books.

"A is for apple," read Mary Jo.

"See apple," said Jimmy.

On through the book Mary Jo read. "B is for book, C is for car, D is for dog."

4 (four)

Mary Jo couldn't believe Jimmy was being so still. "Y is for **yarn**, and Z is for zebra," she ended.

There was no sound from Jimmy.

"Oh, no! He's fast asleep," groaned Mary Jo. "If I call Mom, he'll wake up. What shall I do?"

Mary Jo sat on the floor trying to decide what to do. "I guess I'll just have to sit here, because I can't stand up to carry him to bed."

Before long Mother came. She wondered why it was so quiet. She laughed as she picked Jimmy up to carry him to his bed.

"You are a very good babysitter, Mary Jo," she whispered. "Jimmy didn't bother me or get into any trouble. Thank you for helping."

The order in which things happen in a story is called the sequence of events. If you want to tell a story you have read to someone, it is important to know the right sequence of events.

Complete these activities about sequence of events.

1.1   Put an X by the sentence that is out of sequence. Then number the sentences in the order they happened.

a. _____ Mother put Jimmy to bed.

b. _____ Mary Jo began reading <u>The Alphabet Book</u>.

c. _____ Jimmy helped read.

d. _____ Jimmy fell asleep.

1.2   Number these events from the story, "The Babysitter," in sequence. Read all the sentences first. One and four are done for you.

a. _____ Mary Jo began to read <u>The Alphabet Book</u>.

b. _____ Mother said, "You are a very good babysitter."

c. _____ Mary Jo couldn't move.

     __1__ Mother asked Mary Jo to babysit.

d. _____ Jimmy helped to read the book.

     __4__ Jimmy was very quiet. He had fallen asleep.

e. _____ Mother put Jimmy to bed.

1.3   Jane helps her mother set the table. Read the following sentences and decide what sequence Jane uses to set the table. Write the sentences in the right sequence on the lines.

Next, she put on six plates.

Finally, the glasses go on.

First, Jane put a tablecloth on the table.

After she put on the plates, Jane puts on the knives, forks, and spoons.

Now the table is ready.

a. _____

b. _____

c. _____

d. _____

e. _____

Another important skill you have learned is using context clues. Context clues help you figure out what a word means in a sentence by looking at the words around it.

For example, Mom said that she cannot afford a new dress, because Dad is not working this week.

The words around afford tell you that mother does not have enough money to buy a new dress. You know the meaning of afford by the context clues.

Some words have more than one meaning. Context clues help you to know which meaning is being used.

For example, fast means moving quickly or to go without food.

Daniel ran very fast and won the race.

Daniel went on a fast for three days.

Context clues tell you which meaning to use for fast.

Use context clues and circle the correct meaning of each underlined word.

1.4   Mother asked Mary Jo to <u>care</u> <u>for</u> the baby.

like
pay attention to
take charge of

1.5   Mary Jo <u>continued</u> reading the book.

to do another time
kept on
stayed

1.6   He was <u>fast</u> asleep.

running
deeply, sound
to eat no food

1.7   He is <u>awake</u> now.

aroused
to wake up
not asleep

USING VOWELS

You have learned about using long and short vowels, and how to mark them. Read these rules to help you remember.

1. If a word or syllable has only one vowel and it comes at the beginning or between two consonants, it is usually short.

ăm ĭt răn tăxi

2. If a word or syllable has only one vowel and it comes at the end of the word or syllable, it is usually long.

wē sō pōny tōtal

3. If a word or syllable has two vowels, the first vowel is usually long and the second vowel is silent.

trāin slēep bōat tīme

*Remember, there are always rule breakers—words that do not follow the rules.

Complete this activity.

1.8   Mark the vowels in each word (ō, ŏ). On the line in front of each word, write the number of the rule you used to mark it (1-2-3). Put an X in front of one word that is a rule breaker.

a.	_____ flag	l.	_____ cane
b.	_____ pin	m.	_____ hatch
c.	_____ bake	n.	_____ boat
d.	_____ cab	o.	_____ seven
e.	_____ lake	p.	_____ often
f.	_____ tub	q.	_____ weigh
g.	_____ mule	r.	_____ drum
h.	_____ sail	s.	_____ slide
i.	_____ paper	t.	_____ shrub
j.	_____ robot	u.	_____ cue
k.	_____ geese	v.	_____ tie

Choose the word with the correct vowel and write it on the line.

1.9   The old man walked to the platform with a

_____ .
          (can, cane)

1.10   I make my _____ every morning
                        (bed, bead)
       when I get up.

1.11   At camp we sleep on a _____ .
                                    (cot, coat)

1.12   We will use _____ for our art lesson.
                            (past, paste)

1.13   I _____ all the way to school.
                (rain, ran)

1.14   That dog next door is _____ .
                                    (men, mean)

1.15   The trained_____ did tricks for us.
                        (sell, seal)

1.16   I dropped an ice _____ on the floor.
                                (cub, cube)

1.17   My grandmother is _____ today.
                                (fin, fine)

1.18   We used _____ to tie up the box.
                    (twin, twine)

WRITING SENTENCES

Remember, a sentence must express a complete thought. A sentence always begins with a capital letter. A sentence that tells something ends with a period.

Example: I go to school.

A sentence that asks a question ends with a question mark.

Example: What time is it?

A sentence that expresses excitement ends with an exclamation point.

Example: Watch out for that car!

Cross out each group of words that is not a sentence.

1.19   At the post office.

1.20   Running home.

1.21   When are you coming over?

1.22   The cat is wet.

1.23   are here.

Put the right punctuation mark at the end of each sentence. Circle each letter that should be capitalized.

1.24   where are you going

1.25   i am going home

1.26   my sister is four years old today

1.27   watch out

1.28   what do you have in your sack

1.29	we had fun at your house
1.30	mother, may i go see grandma
1.31	what time is school over
1.32	the sky is falling

Write four sentences in your best handwriting.

1.33   Begin each sentence with a capital letter. Be sure to put a punctuation mark at the end. Make one of your sentences a question.

a. _____

b. _____

c. _____

d. _____

Teacher check _____

                                    Initial   Date

SPELLING

In this spelling section we are reviewing words from Language Arts LIFEPACs 301, 302, and 303. Review Words-301 all have silent letters. Review

Words-302 all have two vowels together, one being long and the other being silent. Review Words-303 all have a vowel and an r together. The sound of the vowel is changed by the r. Sometimes you hear an er-r-r sound and sometimes only the sound of r. Say and study each word carefully.

Spelling Words-1

Review Words-301

knee	fight	wrong
knock	night	write

Review Words-302

beach	maid	speech
speak	goat	float

Review Words-303

herd	nurse	circle	apart
perfect	hurry	cartoon	guard

Complete these spelling activities using Spelling Words-1.

1.34 Write Review Words-301 and circle all the silent letters.

a. _____   d. _____

b. _____   e. _____

c. _____   f. _____

1.35 Write Review Words-302. Mark the long vowels and put a line through the silent vowels.

a. _____   d. _____

b. _____   e. _____

c. _____   f. _____

1.36 Write Review Words-303 under the right heading.

er   **ir**

a. _____   e. _____

b. _____

ur   **ar**

c. _____   f. _____

d. _____   g. _____

                                    h. _____

1.37 Write the words where the vowel plus r make the sound of r.

a. _____   c. _____

b. _____

1.38   Choose five words and write them into sentences. Underline the spelling words.

_____
- -
_____
_____
- -
_____
- -
_____
_____
- -
_____
- -
_____

Teacher check _____

Initial   Date

Ask your teacher to give you a practice spelling test of Spelling Words-1. Restudy the words you missed.

    For this Self Test, study what you have read and done. The Self Test will check what you remember.

SELF TEST 1

Write these sentences in sequence to make a story.

1.01   Grandmother told her it was the Bible.

Then Grandmother picked up the Bible.

First, Ann pointed to a big book on the table.

Grandmother opened the Bible and read to Ann.

Ann asked Grandmother what the book was.

a. _____

b. _____

c. _____

d. _____

e. _____

Draw a circle around the meaning for the underlined word or words.

1.02   A friend <u>loveth at all times.</u> (Proverbs 17:17)

always shows love   always laughs at you

always shares with you

1.03   A rich man's <u>wealth</u> is his strong city. (Proverbs 18:11)

health   money   family

1.04   The baby was <u>fast</u> asleep.

not eating   quickly   sound

1.05   Mary Jo couldn't believe the baby was so <u>still.</u>

even   quiet   noisy

1.06   The <u>game</u> ran through the forest.

        playing ball   wild animals   playing tag

Mark the long and short vowels in these words. Put a line through the silent vowels.

1.07   a. mine   c. Friday   e. freeze

        b. fit   d. cabin   f. we

Write these sentences correctly. Cross out any group of words that is not a sentence.

1.08   today is my birthday

_____

1.09   nine years old

_____

1.010   what time is it

_____

1.011   we have fun at school

_____

1.012   god answers our prayers

_____

1.013   at suppertime

_____

1.014   i had fun at school today

_____

19 / 24

EACH ANSWER, 1 POINT

 Take your Spelling Test for Spelling Words-1.

Teacher check _____

Initial   Date

My Score

II. SECTION TWO

Section two of this LIFEPAC will review reading maps and following directions. You will also review punctuation and capitalization rules. In handwriting you will write tongue twisters. You will review spelling words from Language Arts LIFEPACs 304, 305, and 306.

VOCABULARY

cafetorium	(kaf u tôr′ ē um)	Room used for lunch and meetings.
copied	(kop′ ēd)	One thing made just like another one.
program	(prō ′ gram)	A play or something given for a group of people.

 Ask your teacher to say these words with you.
Teacher check _____

Initial   Date

READING MAPS

We can read different kinds of books and stories. One kind of reading is for fun. Another kind is for study. The story, "Mother's Day Program," is for fun, but it will help you review map reading.

Mother's Day Program

"It won't be long until our mothers come to school for the Mother's Day **program**," said Nancy. "My mother is working, so I invited my grandmother to come. She knows where the school is, but she doesn't know where the **cafetorium** is."

"I didn't think of that," said Suzie. "I'll bet a lot of mothers have never been to the cafetorium."

"Let's ask the teacher if we can make a map so they can get to the right place at two o'clock."

Nancy and Suzie's teacher thought their idea to make a map was very good. The map could be **copied** on a machine in the office so every child could take one home.

Nancy and Suzie set right to work. "North is at the top of a map and south is at the bottom, right?" asked Suzie.

"Yes," said Nancy, "and west is by your left hand and east is toward the right. Let's use abbreviations, okay?"

Before long the map was ready. The girls let the class look at their map to see if it needed any changes.

"That's really good," said Joshua. "You did an excellent job. May I outline it with a dark pencil so Mrs. Jackson can run it through the copy machine?"

"Sure, that would be a great help," answered Suzie.

In a short time each student had this map to take home.

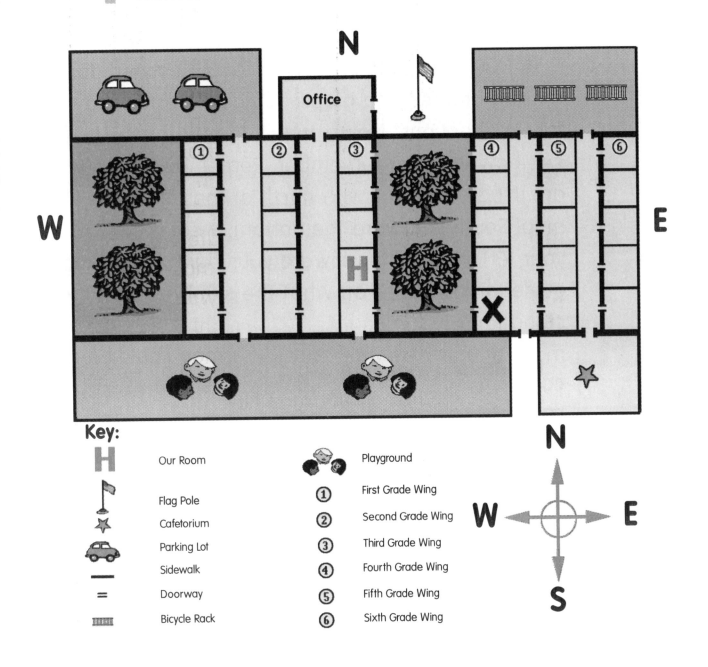

Key:

H	Our Room	Playground	
Flag Pole		①	First Grade Wing
Cafetorium		②	Second Grade Wing
Parking Lot		③	Third Grade Wing
Sidewalk		④	Fourth Grade Wing
Doorway		⑤	Fifth Grade Wing
Bicycle Rack		⑥	Sixth Grade Wing

The teacher said, "Each mother will park in the parking lot when she comes. Matthew, can you tell the class what directions she will need to get from the parking lot to the cafetorium?"

"I'll try," said Matthew. "Let's see. Go east on the sidewalk to the last wing. Turn south and walk to the end of the sidewalk."

"Very good," said the teacher.

In Language Arts LIFEPAC 307, you learned about making and reading maps. You also learned how to follow directions. Now you will review these skills to see how well you remember. Remember that maps are usually laid out with north at the top of the map. South is toward the bottom, west is toward your left, and east is toward your right. Also a map guide, or key, tells you what the symbols on a map stand for.

Example: This map is a drawing of a bedroom. Look at the map key.

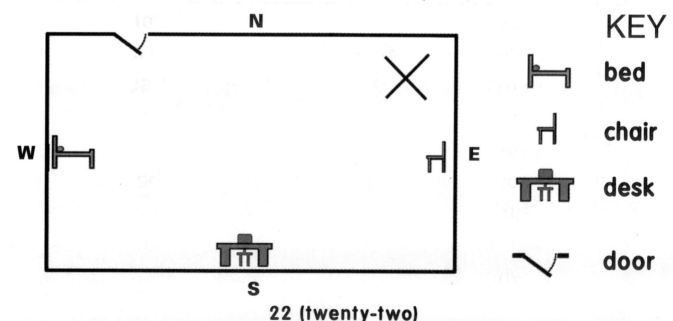

COMPLETE THESE MAP ACTIVITIES.

2.1　Using the map Nancy and Suzie made, write directions like the ones Matthew gave in the story.

a.　how to get to Nancy's room from the parking lot.

_____

_____

b.　how to get to Nancy's room from the bicycle racks.

_____

_____

c.　how to get from the parking lot to the room marked with an X.

_____

_____

Teacher check _____

Initial　　　Date

2.2　Using the map of the school, follow these directions:

a.　You are in the office. Walk out the door by the flagpole. Walk south to the first sidewalk. Turn east and walk to the next wing. Turn south to the second door. Put a blue circle on the room where you would be.

b.　You are in the cafetorium. Walk out the door and turn west. Walk to the last wing. Turn north and go to the third room. Put a red circle on the room where you would be.

23 (twenty-three)

Follow directions.

Look at the puzzle. Some of the letters have squares around them. They are starters. Follow the directions beginning with the starters. Write down each letter you cross. Then write the words you find on the lines in the sentences below the puzzle.

Example: Start with ⬜B. Go right to I, then down to B, down to L, and right to E. The word is Bible.

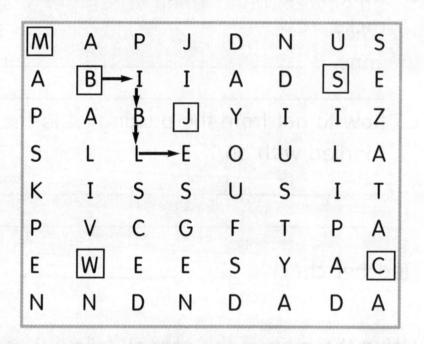

⬜B right, down, down, right. The ___Bible___ is God's Word to us.

2.3 ⬜S up, left, left, down, down.

_____ is the day of rest.

2.4 ⬜J down, down, right, right.

_____ came to save us.

2.5 ⬜W right, down, right, up, right, down, right, up.

_____ comes in the middle of the week.

2.6   C   left, up, up, right, up, left, up, right, up.

_____ the first word in the
sentence.

2.7   M   down, down, down, down, right, up, right, down.

We use _____ to find places on
the maps.

PUNCTUATING SENTENCES

You have learned when to use periods, commas,
question marks, and exclamation points in
sentences. Let's review these punctuation rules.

In several of the LIFEPACs that you have
completed, you have learned about the different
kinds of punctuation. To review, you will find some
lists here to help you remember when to use each
one.

Use a period
___ at the end of a telling sentence. (Please
come in.)
___ after initials. (E. L. Brown)
___ after abbreviations of a title. (Mr., Rev.)
___ after abbreviations for days, months,
streets, cities, and countries (Mon., Apr., St.,
L.A., U.S.)

Use a question mark
___ after an asking sentence. (Where do you
live?)

Use an exclamation mark

____ after a sentence that shows excitement. (Look out!)

____ after words that show strong feeling. (Wow! Look what I found!)

Use a comma

____ after yes or no at the beginning of a sentence. (Yes, I can come.)

____ when a person's name is called. (Mary, come here.)

____ between the name of the city and the state. (Montgomery, Alabama)

____ between the names of a day and the date. (Tuesday, Feb. 6)

____ between the day and the year. (March 12, 1996)

____ between words in a series. (I had corn, chicken, rice, and salad for dinner.)

____ in a letter after the greeting and closing. (Dear Jane, Yours truly,)

Follow the rules and punctuate these sentences. The number at the end of each sentence tells you how many punctuation marks you should make.

2.8   My Uncle John grows corn wheat and hay on his farm (3)

2.9   Mary what do you want for dinner (2)

2.10   Yes you may play basketball (2)

2.11	Jack what time will Bill Tom and Sam get here (4)
2.12	Did you know I came from Dayton Ohio (2)
2.13	I was born on March 2 1988 (2)
2.14	Today is Thursday June 5 1997 (3)
2.15	We have red green blue or yellow paper (4)
2.16	My parents visited Joplin Missouri (2)
2.17	Jack watch out (2)
2.18	Tom please send this box to Las Cruces New Mexico for me (3)

Write eight sentences.

2.19   Each sentence must need at least one comma. Use periods and question marks, too. Write one sentence of exclamation.

a. _____

b. _____

c. _____

d. _____

e. _____

f. _____

g. _____

h. _____

Teacher check _____

Initial   Date

27 (twenty-seven)

CAPITALIZING WORDS

Do you remember all the places to put capital letters? You have been learning about capital letters in all the Language Arts LIFEPACs. Review this Capital Letter Chart from Language Arts LIFEPAC 304.

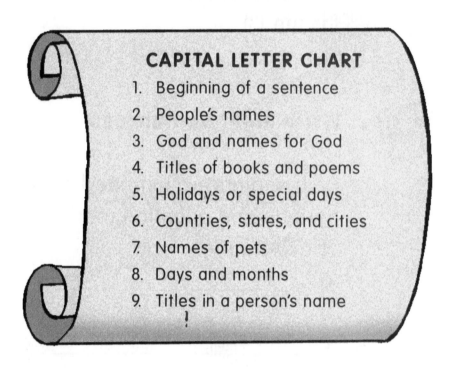

CAPITAL LETTER CHART

1. Beginning of a sentence
2. People's names
3. God and names for God
4. Titles of books and poems
5. Holidays or special days
6. Countries, states, and cities
7. Names of pets
8. Days and months
9. Titles in a person's name

Circle all the letters that should be capitalized. Then rewrite the sentences correctly.

2.20　my aunt lives in memphis, tennessee. (3)

_____

2.21　my sister and i attend lincoln school. (4)

_____

2.22　today is friday, may 6, 1996. (3)

_____

2.23   aunt janie will be here on thursday for christmas. (4)

_____

2.24   i have a cat named tabby and a dog named ruffian. (3)

_____

2.25   i'd like to visit yellowstone national park. (4)

_____

2.26   uncle bob will take us to disneyland. (3)

_____

2.27   mr. jones prays to god every day. (3)

_____

Teacher check _____

                                    Initial   Date

Do this activity.

2.28   Put an X in front of each word that should be capitalized.

a. _____ bus   i. _____ leo
b. _____ mrs. jones   j. _____ february
c. _____ today   k. _____ washington, d.c.
d. _____ wednesday   l. _____ august
e. _____ bozo, the clown   m. _____ lion
f. _____ fine   n. _____ son
g. _____ fido   o. _____ march
h. _____ park

HANDWRITING

Handwriting is a very important communication skill. You need to write clearly so that other people can read what you write.

Use your best handwriting to write a tongue twister.

A tongue twister is a sentence in which many of the words begin with the same sound. If you try to say it very fast, your tongue will get all "mixed up" and the sentence will sound funny. Tongue twisters are fun to read or say. They are fun to write, too.

Say this tongue twister:

Patsy Pansy pranced past the picnic place.

Can you say it without getting your tongue twisted?

Complete these activities.

2.29 Using your best cursive handwriting, copy the tongue twister on these lines.

_____

- -

_____

- -

_____

- -

_____

2.30 Think of some other tongue twisters or make some up. On another piece of paper, write two more in your best handwriting.

Teacher check _____

Initial   Date

SPELLING

In this spelling section you will review words with y used as a vowel and words with the ow spelling. Words with ight and ough are also reviewed. Some words with ie and ei used to spell long ē are included. The plural form of two words that end in f are reviewed as well as words with the /shun/ sound spelled tion. Say each word carefully.

Spelling Words-2

Review Words-304

everybody	bicycle	grown
candy	thrown	frown

Review Words-305

thought	bright	laugh
taught	sight	enough

Review Words-306

vacation	direction	calves	ceiling
station	leaves	receive	neither

---

31 (thirty-one)

Complete these spelling activities with Spelling Words-2.

2.31   Write the words beside the right heading.

a. words with ō   _____

_____

b. words with ī   _____

_____

_____

c. words with ē   _____

_____

_____

d. words with the   _____
    /shun/ sound
_____

_____

e. word with the /ow/
    sound as in ouch   _____

f. words with y used   _____
    as a vowel
_____

_____

2.32   Write calf and leaf. Then write their plural forms.

       a. _____   _____

       b. _____   _____

2.33   What spelling rule can you write telling how to make the plural form for words ending in f?

       When a word ends in f, _____

       _____

2.34   Write three sentences. Use words with ei, augh, and ough. Underline the words you choose.

       a. _____

       _____

       b. _____

       _____

       c. _____

       _____

Teacher check _____

                                Initial   Date

Ask your teacher to give you a practice spelling test of Spelling Words-2. Restudy the words you missed.

Study what you have read and done for this Self Test. This Self Test will check what you remember of this part and other parts you have read.

33 (thirty-three)

SELF TEST 2

Use this map to answer the following questions.

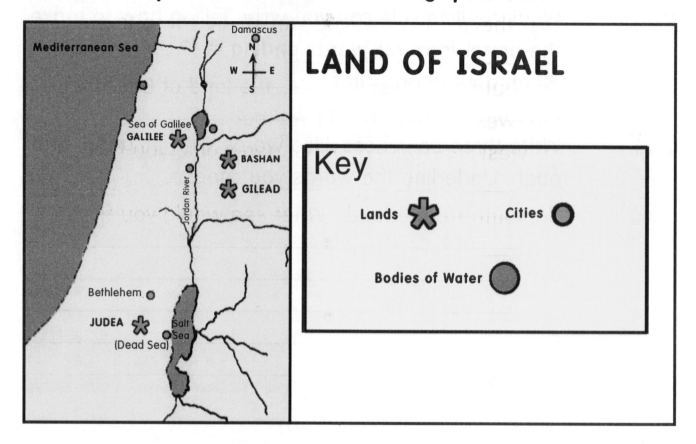

2.01   If you were at the Dead Sea, what direction would you go to get to Gilead? _____

2.02   Which direction would you go to get to Bethlehem?

_____

2.03   Tell how to get to Damascus from Gilead.

_____

2.04   Tell how to go from Galilee to Bashan.

_____

2.05   Tell how to get to the Dead Sea from Damascus.

_____

2.06   What large sea is west of Israel? _____

_____

Use the map to follow these directions.

2.07   Go north from Judea to Galilee. Turn east and go
past the sea. What land would you come to next?

_____

2.08   Go south from Damascus to the land of Bashan.
Turn west. Where would you be? _____

2.09   Go west from Judea. What sea would you find?

_____

2.010   Go south from Gilead. What sea would you find?

_____

Mark the capitals.

2.011   Put an X in front of each word that should be
capitalized.

a. _____ jacob   k. _____ church

b. _____ bible   l. _____ matthew

c. _____ life   m. _____ detroit

d. _____ bethlehem   n. _____ joseph

e. _____ march   o. _____ baby

f. _____ david   p. _____ jesus

g. _____ information   q. _____ monday

h. _____ thursday   r. _____ capital

i. _____ easter   s. _____ mrs.

j. _____ samuel   t. _____ december

Circle every letter that should be capitalized. Put periods, commas, and question marks where they belong. (EACH NUMBERED PROBLEM, 1 POINT)

2.012   my neighbor is mr nickelson (5)

2.013   can you go to aunt sue's house on tuesday (5)

2.014   i live at 647 north pleasant st (5)

2.015   c j smith lives in dayton ohio (9)

2.016   grandma put a sandwich an apple three cookies and some milk in my lunch (5)

2.017   yes your library book is due friday aug 20 1996 (8)

2.018   mary will you watch joey (4)

Mark the long and short vowels. Cross out silent vowels.

2.019   a. mile   c. time   e. maybe   g. laugh

                    b. bit   d. so   f. leaf   h. mane

Write these sentences in the proper sequence.

2.020   I got up early.

                    I got ready for school.

                    The teacher was happy to see us.

                    My friends and I walked to school.

                    I had a good breakfast.

                    a. _____

                    b. _____

                    c. _____

                    d. _____

                    e. _____

Teacher check _____

Initial   Date

My Score

SP_LLING TEST **Take your spelling test of Spelling Words-2.**

III. SECTION THREE

In this section you will read to find the main idea and details to support that idea. Also you will review the cause and effect of some events. Nouns, verbs, adjectives, and adverbs are parts of speech. You will review what kind of words they are and find them in sentences. You will practice good handwriting and letter-writing skills at the same time. Work slowly and do a good job.

VOCABULARY

announce	(u nouns')	Say.
clarinet	(klar u net')	Musical instrument shaped like a tube, played by blowing on a mouthpiece and covering holes with fingers.
eternity	(i tėr' nu tē)	Time without beginning or end.
member	(mem' ber)	Person who belongs to a group.

nervous	(nėr′ vus)	Tense or fearful.
private	(prī′ vit)	Not shared with others.
students	(stü′ dunts)	People in school.

Ask your teacher to say these words with you.
Teacher check _____

Initial   Date

READING FOR COMPREHENSION

Reading to find the main idea of a story and the details that support it is an important reading skill. The main idea of a story is what the story is about. Details help the reader find out more about the main idea. Details are the small things in a story that tell more about the main idea.

As you read the story, "The Tryout," you will know what the main idea is. Try to pay attention to some details about the main idea, too. Ask yourself who, what, and where. The answers to these little questions will be story details.

The Tryout

Today was the day that James was to try out for the All-City Band. For the last three weeks he had done nothing but practice. He knew that not very many people his age became band **members**. The nine- to twelve-year-old **students** were the ones in the school band. James was only eight years old, and he could not be in the school band yet.

LANGUAGE ARTS 310: LIFEPAC TEST

EACH ANSWER, 1 POINT UNLESS OTHERWISE INDICATED

```
68
   85
```

Name _____

Date _____

Score _____

Draw a circle around each noun. **Put a line under each** verb.

1.   Our lunch was a picnic.
2.   The coats were on a chair.
3.   Mother put a patch on my pants.
4.   The clown made a funny face.
5.   My sister cooked chicken for supper.

Put a circle around each adjective. **Put a line under each** adverb.

6.   The tallest person is here.
7.   The funnier clown ran fast.
8.   The big, black bug ran quickly.
9.   The slow turtle walked away.
10.   The pretty, white horse galloped swiftly away.

Read the paragraph. Answer the questions that follow.

Karen wanted her friend, Sandra, to know about Jesus. Karen asked Sandra to go to Sunday school with her. Sandra said, "No," several times, but Karen kept on asking. Finally, Sandra went to a Sunday school picnic with Karen. She listened as the boys and girls played, prayed, and had fun. The next Sunday, Sandra asked if she might go to Sunday school with Karen. Soon she was going regularly. One day Sandra began to ask questions about knowing Jesus. Karen and her mother talked with Sandra. Then . . .

11. What was the outcome of the paragraph?
_____

12. What is the main idea of the paragraph?
_____

13. What are two supporting details?
a. _____
b. _____

14. The effect of the story is that Sandra came to know Jesus. What was one cause?
_____

Draw lines to match the words on the left with words on the right.

15.	reading for fun	atlas
16.	word meanings	fiction
17.	maps	dictionary
18.	information	nonfiction
19.	reading for facts	encyclopedia

Circle the meaning of the underlined words in each sentence.

20. Sandra said, "No," <u>several</u> times.

more than one
thousand
many
none

21. Soon she was going <u>regularly</u>.

not often
each time
absent

22. <u>Finally</u>, Sandra said, "Yes."

the end
at last
always

Put an X in front of each group of words that is not a sentence. Capitalize and punctuate each sentence correctly.

23. _____ the yellow white and black cats ran

24. _____ five little kittens

25. _____ on tuesday may 17 1997 we will go to austin texas

26. _____ yes susan goes to mayfield school

27. _____ are mr and mrs badin your neighbors

Put an X by each title that could be fiction. Put a ✓ by titles that could be nonfiction.

28. _____ Mr. Long Nose

29. _____ Holy Bible

30. _____ World Atlas

31. _____ Mr. Chipmunk Makes a Cake

Alphabetize these words. Then mark the long and short vowels. (EACH WORD, 2 POINTS)

32. wagon   witch   window   woman   wail

a. _____   d. _____

b. _____   e. _____

c. _____

Take your LIFEPAC Spelling Test.

James' parents had given him as much help as they could. When he was only six years old, he had asked if he could take music lessons. Dad wondered if he would practice when the other children were out playing. James was sure that he would. He wanted to be like his older brother, Michael, and play the **clarinet**. So his parents had rented a clarinet and had given him **private** lessons.

Now the time had come to try out for All-City Band. He was the only eight-year-old trying out. James walked into the room. He looked around **nervously** at the three band leaders waiting to hear him. He sat down on the nearest chair, raised the clarinet to his lips and began to play. Soon he forgot his nervousness.

Afterwards James waited with his parents until everyone else had a chance to play. After what seemed like an **eternity**, the new All-City Band members were **announced**. James' name was on the list. He would play third clarinet! James was so happy. Silently he said a little prayer, "Thank you, God, for helping me do my best."

In LIFEPACs 301, 304, 306, 307, and 308 you worked on the main idea and the supporting details of written material. In LIFEPAC 306 you worked on cause and effect in written material.

The main idea of a story might be that Johnny played a good game of baseball. The supporting details might be that he came early to practice. He listened to the coach and he hit a home run or two. The effect of the story might be that he felt very good about the game. The cause of the story might be that Johnny was very interested in baseball. He practiced hard every day. He did exactly as the coach asked.

You may want to go back and review some of these lessons before trying to do these activities.

Circle the main idea of the story, "The Tryout."

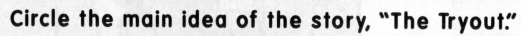

3.1   James played the clarinet.
All-City Band members had to try out.
James was given a place in the All-City Band.

Put an X in front of all the details in the story.

3.2 Each detail must support the main idea.

a. _____ James practiced very hard.

b. _____ James' parents helped him.

c. _____ Michael played clarinet too.

d. _____ James started taking music lessons early.

e. _____ Boys and girls played outdoors.

f. _____ James was nervous, but began to play well.

g. _____ James said thank you to God for helping him do his best.

3.3 The effect is that James was given a place in the All-City Band. Write four sentences that could be the cause of his becoming a band member.

a. _____

b. _____

c. _____

d. _____

Teacher check _____

Initial   Date

REVIEWING PARTS OF SPEECH

In LIFEPACs 304, 307, 308, and 309 you studied the parts of speech: nouns, verbs, adjectives, and adverbs.

It would be a good idea to go back and review the lessons in these LIFEPACs before you do these activities.

Nouns name people, places, or things (boy, town, apple).

Verbs are action words (run, sit, fly, cry) or being words (am, is, are, was, were).

Adjectives are words that describe nouns. They tell how many, what kind, and which one (six, blue, that, big, fat).

Adverbs are words that limit or add to the meaning of verbs. They tell how, when, and where (down, quickly, cheerfully).

Put a line under each noun and a circle around each verb in these sentences.

3.4   The big zebras ran down the hill.

3.5   Marjorie ran and skipped all the way to school.

3.6   The teacher shut the door.

3.7   The dogs and cats were running and playing in the yard.

3.8   The baby screamed and cried.

3.9   This funny monkey jumped up and down.

3.10   The boys and girls played baseball.

3.11   Mom turned the light off.

Add adjectives to these sentences to make them more interesting (remember that adjectives tell how many, what kind, and which one).

3.12   The _____ giraffe lives in the zoo.

3.13   A _____ tree is growing in our yard.

3.14   My _____ friend will come over.

3.15   That _____ boy is my cousin.

3.16   There were _____ dogs in the dog show.

3.17   There are _____ girls in my classroom.

3.18   This page has _____ questions.

3.19   The man carried _____ packages.

Add adverbs to these sentences to tell how, when, or where. You may use words from the box or you may use words of your own.

carefully	slowly	completely
nearby	everywhere	never
always	yesterday	today
quickly	fast	well

3.20   My birthday was _____ .

3.21   My dad _____ wears a hat.

3.22   I looked _____ for my books.

3.23   My grandmother lives _____ .

3.24   The water ran _____ down the creek.

3.25   Please hold this cup _____ .

3.26   The turtle crawled _____ away from us.

3.27   James plays the clarinet _____ .

Write four interesting sentences.

3.28   Write sentences with four parts of speech (noun, verb, adjective, and adverb).

a. _____

   _____

b. _____

   _____

c. _____

   _____

d. _____

   _____

Teacher check _____

Some verbs are called helping verbs. They are used with an action verb. Some helping verbs are has, have, had, is, am, **are**, **was**, and were.

Examples: is going
was running
Dad **was** driving the car.

To balance this scale, you must write a sentence on the other side that is equal to the one given. The sentence you write must have a helping verb. (I did the dishes today.—I have done the dishes.) (I cut the meat.—I have cut the meat).

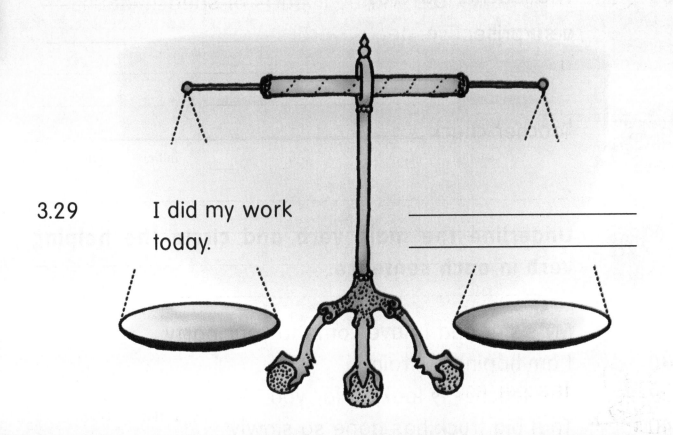

3.29   I did my work today.   _____

3.30 I grew tomatoes in _____

my garden. _____

3.31 I sang in the choir. _____

_____

3.32 I took my book to _____

the library. _____

3.33 I wrote a letter to _____

my grandparents. _____

3.34 I saw a falling star. _____

_____

3.35 My sister went to _____

a movie. _____

3.36 The teacher gave us _____

a surprise. _____

Teacher check _____

Initial   Date

Underline the main verb and circle the helping verb in each sentence.

3.37 My sister and I have come to your party.
3.38 I am hoping for rain.
3.39 The teacher is looking for you.
3.40 That big truck has gone so slowly.

3.41	I have looked everywhere for my glasses.
3.42	The rain was dripping from the roof.
3.43	The pancakes I made were burned.
3.44	My grandpa has gone home.
3.45	Jimmy has paid for the tickets.
3.46	You have broken your new toy.

 Write helping verbs in these sentences.

3.47	All of the school buses _____ gone.
3.48	I _____ writing a letter to my friend.
3.49	The Smiths _____ gone to the beach.
3.50	_____ you ever run in a race?
3.51	Janet _____ run the wrong way.
3.52	I _____ seen this picture before.
3.53	_____ your mother ever been on a subway?
3.54	The workers _____ gone home early.

 **WRITING LETTERS**

You will practice using good handwriting skills and letter-writing skills together. You can review how to write letters from Language Arts LIFEPACs 307 and 309.

Remember that a letter has five main parts: heading, greeting, body, closing, and signature.

Complete these activities. Use your best handwriting.

3.55   Name the five parts of a letter.

      a. _____

      b. _____

      c. _____

      d. _____

      e. _____

3.56   Write these parts of a letter using the correct
      punctuation and capitalization.

      a.   752 n 10th st

                   phoenix arizona 85018

                   may 2 1997

                   _____

                   _____

                   _____

      b.   dear uncle joe

         _____

      c.   with love

                   _____

      d.   jimmy

                   _____

3.57   Use a piece of writing paper to write a friendly letter. Follow these suggestions. You may use some of your own ideas also.

     a. Ask a friend to spend Saturday night and attend Sunday school with you the next day.

     b. Tell your grandparents about your school.

     c. Tell your parents how glad you are that they are your parents.

     d. Invite a friend to a party.

     e. Ask your mom to come have lunch with you at school.

3.58   Use another piece of paper to write a thank-you letter. Again you are given some suggestions if you choose to use one.

     a. Thank someone for a birthday gift.

     b. Thank someone for taking you to the park or zoo.

     c. Thank someone for letting you come for a visit.

     d. Thank someone for making you a toy, dress, or shirt.

     e. Thank someone (your teacher) for something she has done for you.

Teacher check _____

                                    Initial   Date

     Study what you have read and done for this Self Test. This Self Test will check what you remember of this part and other parts you have read.

SELF TEST 3

Read this paragraph. Draw a line under the sentence that tells the main idea.

3.01   Samson knew that God had a special plan for his life. Samson was a very strong man. He was sent to free his people from their enemies. Samson was able to break any rope that held him down. His enemies could not catch him. Samson sinned and he was not strong anymore. Later he was sorry. Once more, Samson became strong and did God's work.

Put an X in front of each supporting detail to the main idea.

3.02   The details are

    a. _____ Samson was to set his people free.

    b. _____ Samson was very strong.

    c. _____ Samson lived a long, long time ago.

    d. _____ Samson did God's work.

    e. _____ Samson sinned, but was sorry later.

Put an X **in front of each right answer.**

3.03 The effect of Samson's work is that God's people were freed from the enemy. Choose the sentences that might have been the cause.

a. _____ Samson knew God.

b. _____ Samson was a big, strong man

c. _____ Samson did God's work.

d. _____ Samson met Delilah.

Read the paragraph. Then classify all boxed words as nouns, adjectives, verbs, or adverbs.

One $\boxed{\text{day}}$ $\boxed{\text{Jack}}$ was $\boxed{\text{quietly}}$ $\boxed{\text{playing}}$ a $\boxed{\text{game.}}$ He saw a $\boxed{\text{yellow}}$ $\boxed{\text{truck}}$ $\boxed{\text{stop}}$ $\boxed{\text{suddenly}}$ at his $\boxed{\text{house}}$ He $\boxed{\text{ran}}$ $\boxed{\text{fast}}$ down the $\boxed{\text{street.}}$ He $\boxed{\text{saw}}$ the $\boxed{\text{big}}$ $\boxed{\text{delivery}}$ $\boxed{\text{truck}}$ leaving. Jack $\boxed{\text{quickly}}$ $\boxed{\text{ran}}$ inside. The truck $\boxed{\text{had}}$ $\boxed{\text{come}}$ to deliver his $\boxed{\text{new,}}$ $\boxed{\text{red}}$ $\boxed{\text{bicycle.}}$

3.04 nouns _____

3.05 verbs _____

3.06 adjectives _____

3.07 adverbs _____

Circle the helping verb in each sentence.

3.08 Our ice cream is melting.

3.09 Our neighbors are moving.

3.010 My lunch money was found in my pockets.

3.011 Billy and Nancy were riding bicycles.

3.012   I am praying that Aunt Jane asks Jesus into her heart.

3.013   My grandmother has given me a new Bible.

3.014   I think all of the boys and girls have gone home.

3.015   Mr. Alberts had cleaned our room.

Mark each long and short vowel. Cross out each silent vowel.

3.016   a. made   b. mean   c. maybe

3.017   a. maid   b. mad   c. mane

3.018   a. mix   b. might   c. met

Circle the meaning of the underlined word.

3.019   A <u>mole</u> was digging a tunnel in our yard.

an animal
a dark spot
mark on the face
feathers

3.020   Father saw a <u>tuft</u> of grass turn brown.

bunch growing together
top of soil
used to pour
water

3.021   After awhile the <u>tunnel</u> was long.

music
underground road

3.022	The mole wanted to <u>modify</u> the size of his home.	move change leave alone

3.023	Father decided to <u>rid</u> our yard of moles.	fit out clear out sound out

Number these sentences in sequence.

3.024 _____ First we said the pledge to the flag.

3.025 _____ After we prayed, Miss Smith read from the Bible.

3.026 _____ The bell rang and school began.

3.027 _____ Then we prayed.

3.028 _____ Now we were ready to have mathematics.

Rewrite these sentences on the lines; capitalize and punctuate correctly (one point for each sentence).

3.029   the red yellow blue and green crayons are here (5)

3.030   what time will suzie leave (3)

3.031   my aunt jane lives in salem oregon (7)

3.032   the letter came on april 2 1997 (4)

3.033   is mr e l smith your neighbor (9)

3.034   yes we live in the u s a now (9)

50 / 63

EACH ANSWER, 1 POINT

Teacher check _____

Initial   Date

My Score

54 (fifty-four)

IV. SECTION FOUR

In Section Four you will review fiction and nonfiction material. You will also review the different kinds of reference books and their uses. You will review how to alphabetize words and how to write a paragraph. Spelling words from three other LIFEPACs are reviewed also.

ability	(a bil' u t ē)	Power to do.
chores	(chôrz)	Odd jobs.
general	(jen' ur ul)	Officer of high rank.
organized	(ôr' gun īzd)	Put together in an orderly way.
popular	(pop' yu lur)	Pleasing to many people.
requires	(ri kwīrz')	Has need of.
scored	(skôrd)	Points made.
sports	(spôrts)	Games.
vacant	(vā' kunt)	Empty, not having anything in it.

Ask your teacher to say these words with you.
Teacher check _____

Initial   Date

READING FOR FUN

All of the reading that people do can usually be divided into two kinds of reading. People read for fun because they enjoy reading, or people read to get information. Stories, like those in library books, that are not really true are called fiction. Fiction is read for fun.

Read "The Game of Baseball." It is a short fiction story.

The Game of Baseball

One Saturday morning Jaime couldn't think of a thing to do. Her morning tasks were done, so she asked her mother what she could do. Her mother suggested that she could help her brother with his **chores**. Jaime really didn't have that in mind, but she got to work and soon they had his work done, too.

"I'll bet I can find some friends to play baseball," said her brother. "Why don't you ask your friends to come and we'll have a game at school on the baseball diamond."

It wasn't too long before quite a few boys and girls were at the school ready to play baseball. The teams were chosen and Jaime's team took the field. Three people got hits and two runs were **scored**. But finally, there were three outs. Playing baseball was fun. Jaime was glad her brother had thought of doing this!

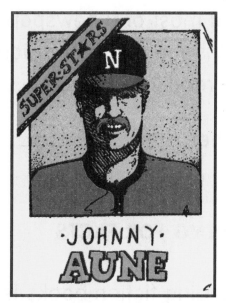

·JOHNNY· AUNE

The game went very well for awhile, but then Kenny said that he was not out on first base and Keith said that he was.

Jaime didn't know what to do. She didn't want them to quarrel. No one was having any fun now, so she. . .

Predict the outcome.

4.1 Write in your own words on another piece of paper an ending for this story.

Teacher check _____

Initial   Date

Answer these questions.

4.2 What is fiction? _____

4.3 Is the story "Little Red Riding Hood" fiction? _____

4.4 Is the Bible fiction? _____

4.5   Would most of a newspaper be fiction? _____

4.6   What is the name of a fiction story or book you have read lately? _____

Teacher check _____

Initial   Date

READING FOR FACTS

Reading fiction books is usually reading for fun. If a person wants some information or wants to learn something, that person usually reads nonfiction. A nonfiction book is true. A nonfiction book or story is factual. It tells information.

Most newspaper stories are nonfiction. Science and social studies books are nonfiction. The dictionary and encyclopedia are nonfiction. Any story that is true is nonfiction.

Here is another story about baseball. It has the same title as the first one you read, but this story is factual. This story is nonfiction.

The Game of Baseball

Baseball is called the national game of the United States. Abner Doubleday, who later became a **general** in the army, is the person who is said to have started the game.

Baseball became very **popular** fast. It is one of the best **organized** games in American **sports**, but it also can be played by most people in a **vacant** lot, in a park, or even in a backyard anywhere.

Baseball **requires** some skills such as throwing and running. The **ability** to catch and to bat requires good eyesight.

The game has spread to many countries of the world. American soldiers and sailors in World War II played it in their "free" time. The people in those countries watched them and they learned the game, too.

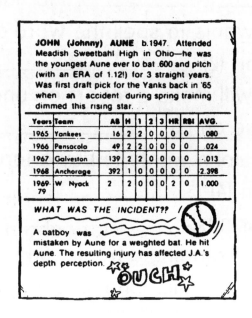

JOHN (Johnny) AUNE b.1947. Attended Meadish Sweetbahl High in Ohio—he was the youngest Aune ever to bat .600 and pitch (with an ERA of 1.12!) for 3 straight years. Was first draft pick for the Yanks back in '65 when an accident during spring training dimmed this rising star. . .

Years	Team	AB	H	1	2	3	HR	RBI	AVG.
1965	Yankees	16	2	2	0	0	0	0	.080
1966	Pensacola	49	2	2	0	0	0	0	.024
1967	Galveston	139	2	2	0	0	0	0	-.013
1968	Anchorage	392	1	0	0	0	0	0	2.398
1969-79	W. Nyack	2	2	0	0	0	2	0	1.000

WHAT WAS THE INCIDENT??

A batboy was mistaken by Aune for a weighted bat. He hit Aune. The resulting injury has affected J.A.'s depth perception. OUCH

This story, "The Game of Baseball," could have come from an encyclopedia. In Language Arts LIFEPAC 309 you learned that an encyclopedia is one kind of reference book. Dictionaries and an atlas are reference books, too. A dictionary is a book of words and an atlas is a book of maps. Reference books are nonfiction. Reference books give facts on subjects that are in alphabetical order.

 Write the name of a reference book on each line. Then fit the words into the puzzle. (Words go across only.)

4.7   Jane is moving to a new town. She would use the (1) _____ to find where this town is.

4.8   Jody wants to spell the word **dinosaur**. He would use the (2) _____ .

4.9   Alice will make a report on undersea animals. She will use an (3) _____ .

4.10   Uncle John wants to buy a farm in Iowa. He would use an (4) _____ to find out where the farm is.

4.11   Mom is reading a book. She wants to find out what a word means. She would use the (5) _____ _____ .

4.12   Charlie wants to find out about tornadoes. He would use an (6) _____ .

Write fiction **or** nonfiction **on the line.**

4.13 _____ The Bible

4.14 _____ the dictionary

4.15 _____ a map

4.16 _____ most of the newspaper

4.17 _____ "Cinderella"

4.18 _____ most comic books

4.19 _____ what people read for fun

4.20 _____ what people read for facts

ALPHABETIZING

In order to find information in reference books, you must know how to alphabetize words—put them in the order of the alphabet.

Write these words in alphabetical order.

4.21 morning   tasks
     friends   Saturday
     chores   brother

a. _____ d. _____

b. _____ e. _____

c. _____ f. _____

4.22

encyclopedia	dictionary
atlas	Bible
newspaper	maps
a. _____	d. _____
b. _____	e. _____
c. _____	f. _____

It is very easy to alphabetize a group of words when every word begins with a different letter. Sometimes several words will begin with the same letter. Alphabetize them by looking at the second letter.

Example: Words: mother, Mary, men.

Alphabetical
order: Mary, men, mother

All these words begin with m. They are alphabetized by the second letter. If more than one word has the second letter the same, look at the third letter to alphabetize.

Example: Words: Mary, mother,
money, moon, men.

Alphabetical
order: Mary, men, money,
moon, mother.

In these words Mary and men came first by the second letters a and e. Then came the mo words.

Look at the third letter. Money comes before moon, because n comes before o. Mother is last, because t in mother comes after o in moon.

Write these words in alphabetical order.

4.23

Jesus
Jacob
Judah

Jews
Jerusalem
Joshua

a. _____
b. _____
c. _____

d. _____
e. _____
f. _____

4.24

school
Saturday
Suzie

scored
she
someone

a. _____
b. _____
c. _____

d. _____
e. _____
f. _____

4.25

people
baseball
brother
bat

quarrel
diamond
runs
boys

a. _____
b. _____
c. _____
d. _____

e. _____
f. _____
g. _____
h. _____

4.26

army	country
played	park
ability	catching
people	soldiers
sailors	sports
skills	sat

a. _____ g. _____

b. _____ h. _____

c. _____ i. _____

d. _____ j. _____

e. _____ k. _____

f. _____ l. _____

WRITING PARAGRAPHS

In Language Arts LIFEPAC 308 you learned how to write a paragraph. A paragraph is three or more sentences about the same topic. Every paragraph has a main idea and some details to support it. The details are written in sequence or in order to make good sense.

Read this paragraph to find the main idea and the details.

Andrew

Andrew was one of Jesus' disciples. Andrew is remembered for bringing people to Jesus. Andrew brought his brother, Peter, to Jesus, and Peter became a disciple. Andrew also brought a little boy to Jesus who had a lunch of five small loaves of bread and two fishes. Jesus took the little boy's lunch and fed more than five thousand people. Andrew was a good disciple.

 Do these activities.

4.27   Underline the sentence that tells the main idea of the paragraph, "Andrew."

4.28   Put an X beside each detail that supports the main idea.

    a. _____ was a disciple

    b. _____ brought Peter to Jesus

    c. _____ Peter became a disciple

    d. _____ brought a boy to Jesus

    e. _____ was a good disciple

    f. _____ the lunch was five loaves and two fishes

Write a paragraph.

4.29   Choose a topic. Use one of these or one of your own.
        Write the topic on the line.

       a. _____   a picnic

       b. _____   your pet

       c. _____   your favorite person

       d. _____   how you came to know Jesus

       e. _____   your grandpa or grandma

       f. _____   what you like to do most

       g. _____

4.30   Now write five details about your topic.

       a. _____   d. _____

       b. _____   e. _____

       c. _____

4.31   Now write a sentence about the main idea you chose.
        Then write the details into sentences. Write the
        sentences in a paragraph. Be sure to capitalize and
        punctuate each sentence.

        _____

        _____

        _____

        _____

4.32 Read the paragraph you wrote. Is every first word of a sentence capitalized? Is there a period or question mark after each sentence? Are the words all spelled correctly? Correct all the mistakes. Now copy your paragraph in your very best handwriting.

_____

_____

_____

_____

_____

_____

_____

_____

_____

_____

_____

Teacher check _____

SPELLING

Review spelling words from Language Arts
LIFEPACs 307, 308, and 309. The words from
Language Arts LIFEPAC 307 all have -er, -est, -ing,
and -ed endings. Words from Language Arts
LIFEPAC 308 are compound words and words that
end in a consonant plus le. Language Arts LIFEPAC
309 Review Words all have a prefix or a suffix
added.

Study these words and do the activities. Be ready
to take the big review test.

Review Words-307

invited	clapping	ripest
sneezing	fresher	coolest

Review Words-308

gingerbread	cornfield	vegetable
somebody	upstairs	saddle

Review Words-309

uncover	disappear	darkness	fourteen
remodel	sleepless	handful	fifteen

Do these spelling activities using Spelling Words-3.

4.33   Write the compound words. Draw a line between the two words that make each one compound.

a. _____   c. _____

b. _____   d. _____

4.34   Write the words that have a final e dropped and an ending added.

a. _____   c. _____

b. _____

4.35   Write the word that has the final consonant doubled and an ending added. _____

4.36   Write the words that have a prefix.

a. _____   c. _____

b. _____

4.37   Write all the words that have a suffix added. Draw a circle around the root word.

a. _____   g. _____

b. _____   h. _____

c. _____   i. _____

d. _____   j. _____

e. _____   k. _____

f. _____

4.38   Write the words that end in le and mark the syllables.

a. _____   b. _____

4.39   Write two sentences. Use three words of your choice in each sentence. Underline the spelling words.

a. _____

_____

b. _____

_____

Ask a teacher to give you a practice spelling test of Spelling Words-3. Restudy the words you missed.

Study what you have read and done for this Self Test. This Self Test will check what you remember in your studies of all parts in this LIFEPAC. The last Self Test will tell you what parts of the LIFEPAC you need to study again.

SELF TEST 4

Use words from the box and write answers to the riddles on the lines.

alphabetical order	dictionary
encyclopedia	atlas
nonfiction	fiction

4.01   I am in a library. I am fun to read. What kind of book am I?

_____

4.02   I am in a library. You use me to study. I give you facts and information. What kind of book am I?

_____

4.03   I am a skill you are learning. You can use me for finding words in a dictionary. What am I?

_____

4.04   I am a book. I have maps. What am I?

_____

4.05   I am a book. I tell meanings of words. What am I?

_____

4.06   I am also a book. I tell lots of information about different subjects. What am I?

_____

4.07   The main words on our pages are in alphabetical order. What are we? an a. _____ and a b. _____

Put an X in front of each statement that is true.

4.08   _____ A funny story about talking animals is fiction.

4.09   _____ Charlotte's Web is nonfiction.

4.010   _____ Information in an encyclopedia is nonfiction.

4.011   _____ Stories about animals can be fiction or nonfiction.

4.012   _____ Fiction books are read for fun.

4.013   _____ Reference books are for study.

4.014   _____ A thank-you letter is a type of fiction.

4.015 _____ Atlases are nonfiction.

4.016 _____ You can find out about animals in an encyclopedia.

Write the answers to these questions on the lines.

4.017   What part of a map is usually north?

_____

4.018   How can you tell what map symbols mean?

_____

4.019   What is a main idea of a story?

_____

4.020   What are supporting details of a story?

_____

Write these words in alphabetical order.

4.021   Genesis   Leviticus   Judges
         Ruth   Ezra   Proverbs
         Job   Psalms   Ecclesiastes

a. _____   f. _____

b. _____   g. _____

c. _____   h. _____

d. _____   i. _____

e. _____

4.022   Write a paragraph about the best present you ever received. The paragraph should be at least three sentences long but not more than six.

_____

_____

_____

_____

_____

_____

_____

_____

_____

_____

_____

_____

_____

_____

_____

Capitalize and punctuate these sentences correctly.

4.023   when will the plane leave minot north dakota (6)

4.024   send this package to mrs c v brown in pueblo colorado (12)

4.025   my next birthday will be august 7 2004 (4)

4.026   we had hamburgers corn salad brownies and peaches for lunch (6)

4.027   on tuesday june 6 my grandmother will come to visit (6)

4.028   david please be here on sept 12 (5)

4.029   no i dont think you should go (5)

Put these words in alphabetical order. Then mark the vowels.

4.030   sleep   stem   skate   slide   skip

             a. _____

             b. _____

             c. _____

             d. _____

             e. _____

Circle the nouns in the sentences. Put one line under each verb.

4.031   The big black car came quickly down the street.

4.032   The red bicycle is broken.

4.033   The mouse ran swiftly and quietly.

4.034   The tired pony trotted slowly.

4.035   The fat dog barked loudly at the cat.

Write all the adjectives and adverbs in the sentences (4.031 through 4.035) on these lines.

	adjectives		adverbs
4.036	a. _____	b.	_____
4.037	a. _____	b.	_____
4.038	a. _____	b.	_____
4.039	a. _____	b.	_____
4.040	a. _____	b.	_____

50 / 63

EACH ANSWER, 1 POINT

Teacher check _____

Initial   Date

My Score

Take your Spelling Test for Spelling Words-3.

Before taking the LIFEPAC Test, you should do these self checks.

1. Did you do good work on your last Self Test?

2. Did you study again those parts of the LIFEPAC you didn't remember?

   Check one: ☐   Yes (good)
                    ☐   No (ask your teacher)

3. Do you know all the new words in "Vocabulary"?

   Check one: ☐   Yes (good)
                    ☐   No (ask your teacher)

4. Can you spell all your new spelling words?

   Check one: ☐   Yes (good)
                    ☐   No (ask your teacher)

NOTES